The Magic Numbers

www.themagicnumbers.net

Design by CC-Lab and The Magic Numbers
Band illustration by Pete Fowler

Printed in England by Caligraving Ltd
All rights reserved

Music arranged by Matt Cowe, Alex Davis and Andrew Mockler
Music processed by Bassline

Edited By Lucy Holliday and Matt Gates

ISBN 0-571-52490-7

To buy Faber Music publications or to find out
about the full range of titles available,
please contact your local music retailer
or Faber Music sales enquiries:

Faber Music Ltd,
Burnt Mill, Elizabeth Way,
Harlow, CM20 2HX England
Tel: +44 (0) 1279 82 89 82
Fax: +44 (0) 1279 82 89 83
sales@fabermusic.com
fabermusic.com

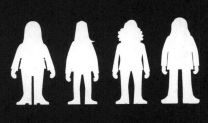

MORNINGS ELEVEN

Words and Music by Romeo Stodart and Michele Stodart

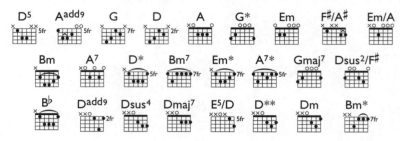

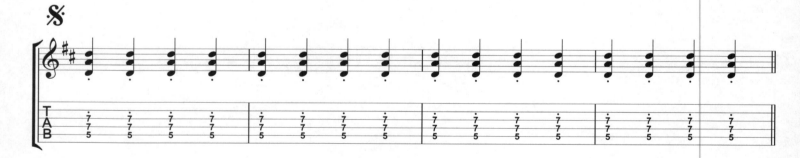

4. What's my name? What's my name? What's my name? What's my name? What's my name? What's my name?

1,3. You're in de-nial,___   you're in de-nial_____ and I know.

2,4. Well what's my_ name?   Well what's my_ name?_____ I don't

FOREVER LOST

Words and Music by Romeo Stodart

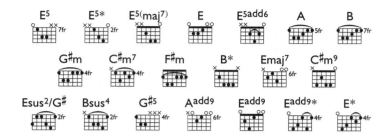

1. Dar - ling,___ what you gon - na do now,___ now that you no -
2. Dar - ling,___ what you gon - na say now,___ now that you no -

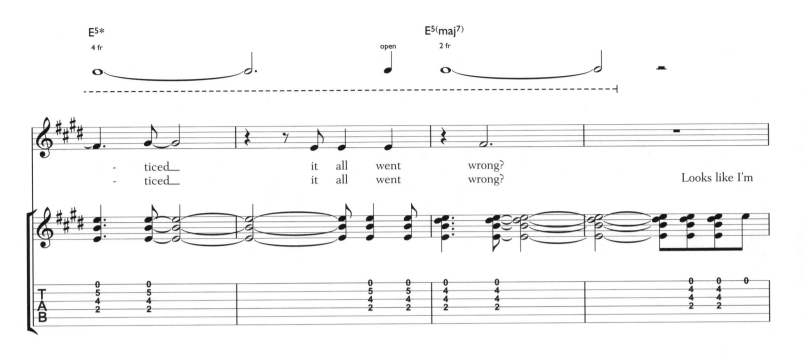

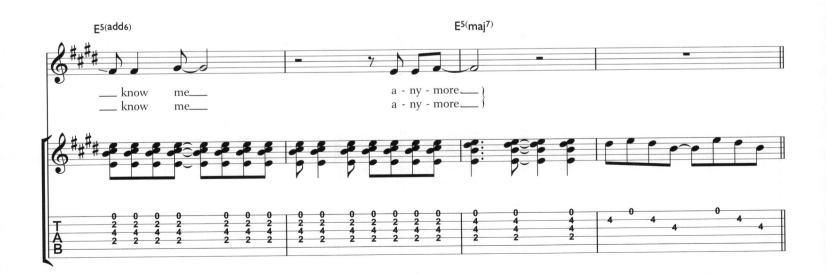

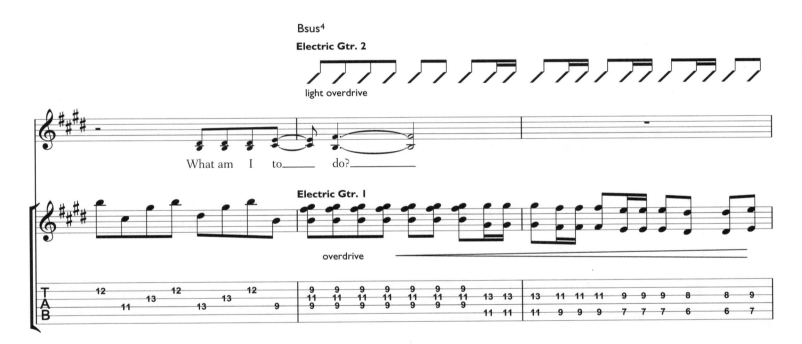

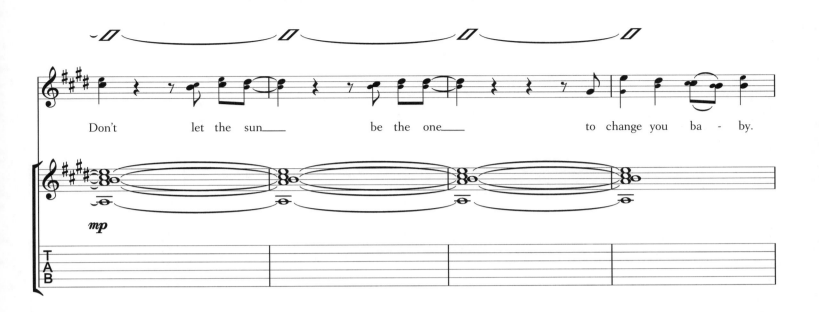

Don't   let the sun___   be the one___   to change you ba - by.

A   B   G#m   C#m7

I   wan-na learn___   how to lie___   if I'm to__ know.   'Cos

Bass arr. for Electric Gtr. 2

Electric Gtr. 1

clean

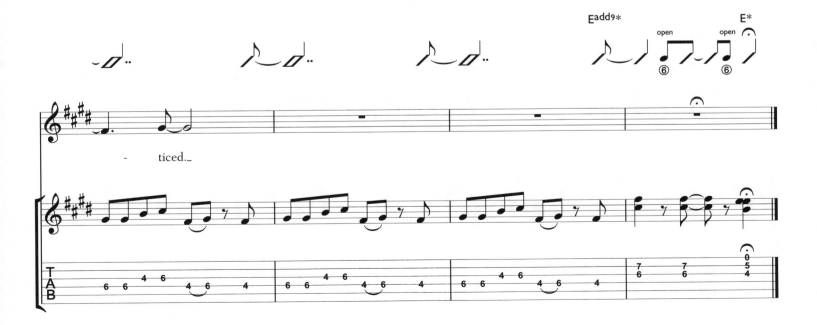

THE MULE

Words and Music by Romeo Stodart

1. How ma-ny times__ must you call__ me in the morn-ing be-fore I__ wake up?
2. How ma-ny times__ must I stum-ble in___ drunk be-fore you__ scold me?

1.2.3. One more drink and I'll___ be fine.___ One more girl to take___ you off my mind.___
4. one more girl and I'll___ be fine.___ One more drink to take___ you off my mind.___

1.2.3.

(3° only)

(3.) Oh,_____

4.

LONG LEGS

Words and Music by Romeo Stodart

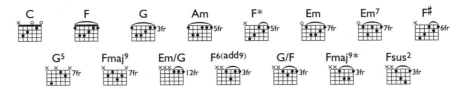

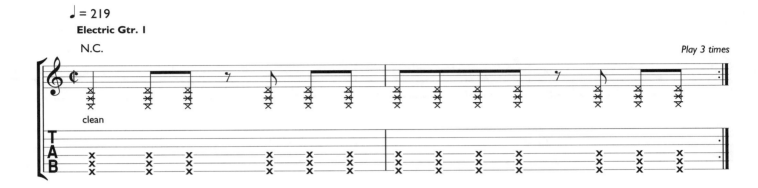

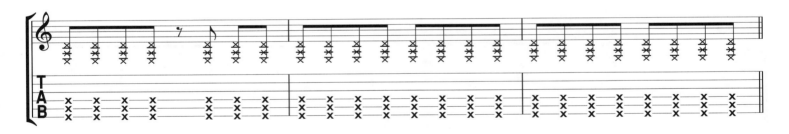

1. Long legs,_____ don't give me no head rush in ____ the
(2.) bad, too bad_____ and I don't think I'll ev- er feel the same a- gain.
3. Long legs,_____ don't give me no head rush in ____ the

To Coda ⊕

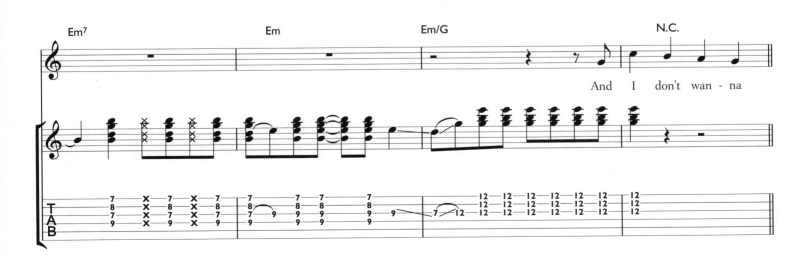

And I don't wan - na

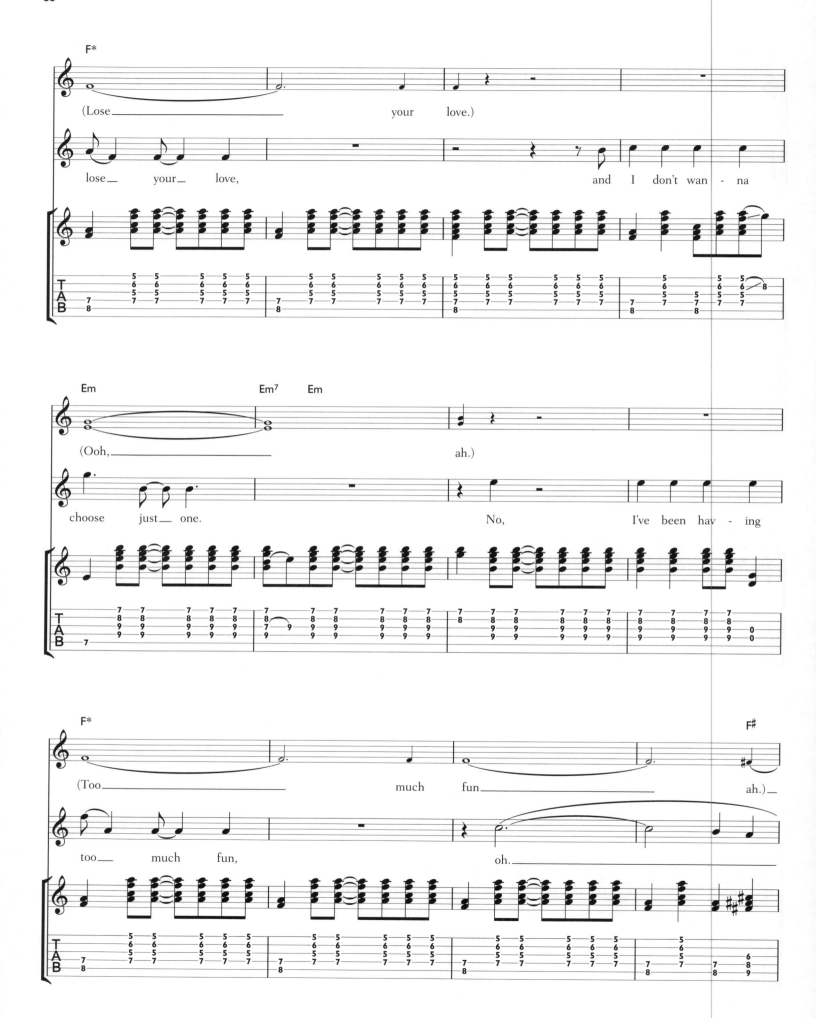

D.℠ al Coda

Coda

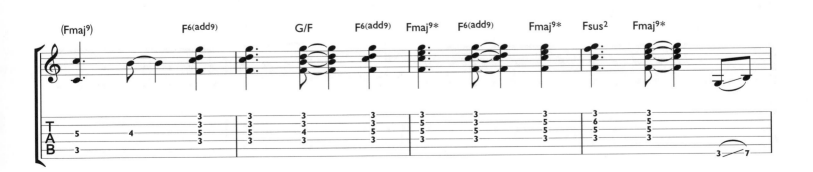

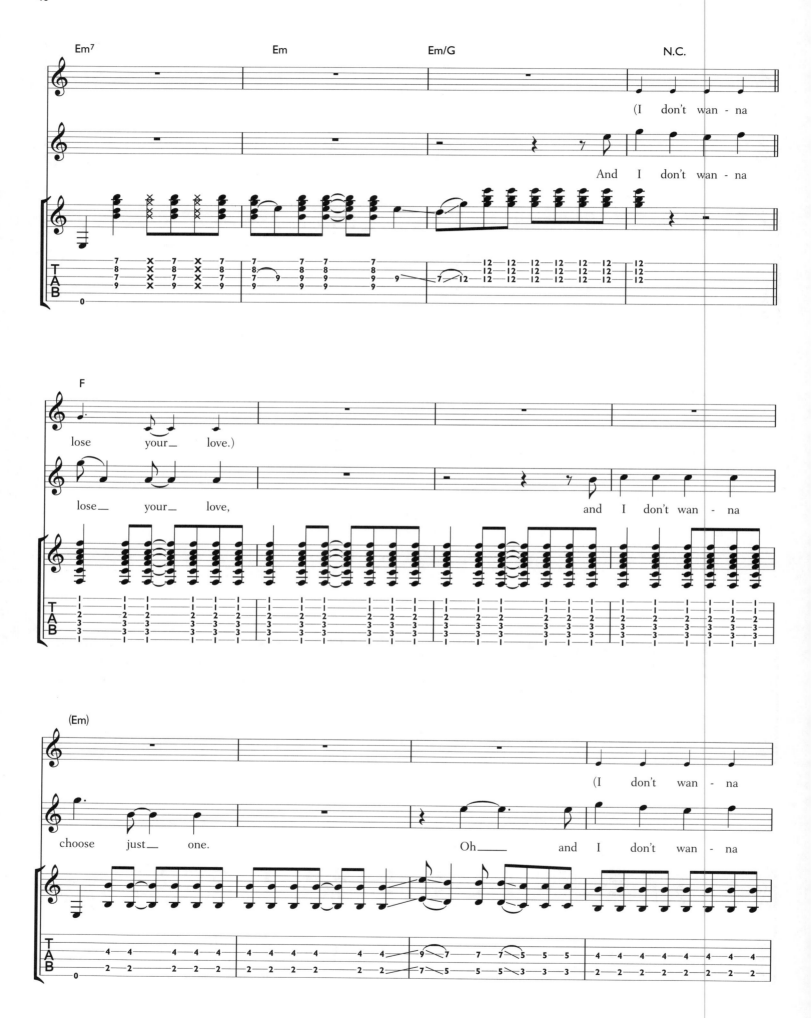

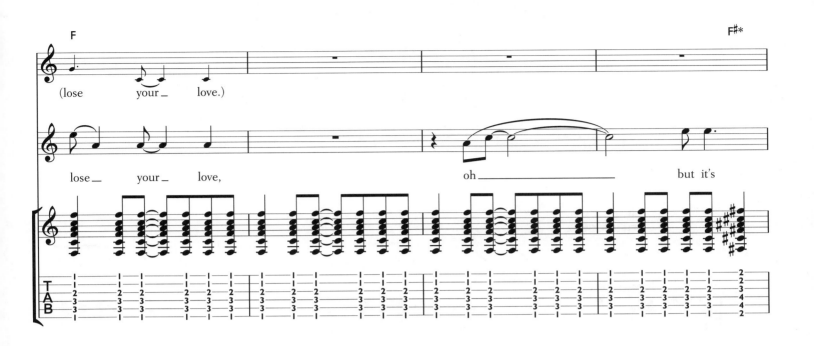

LOVE ME LIKE YOU

Words and Music by Romeo Stodart

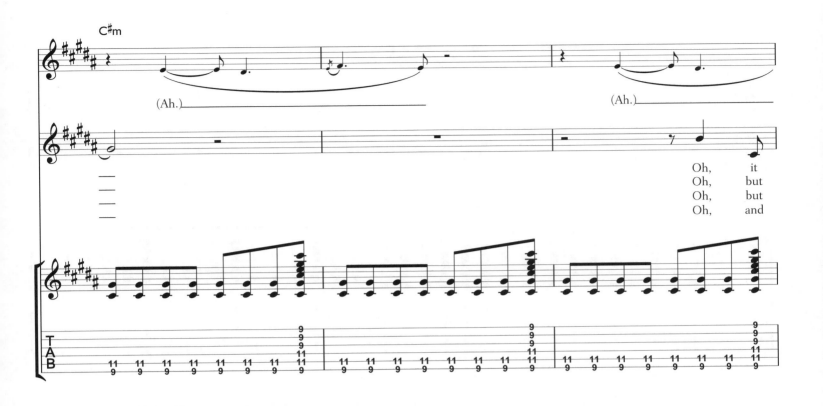

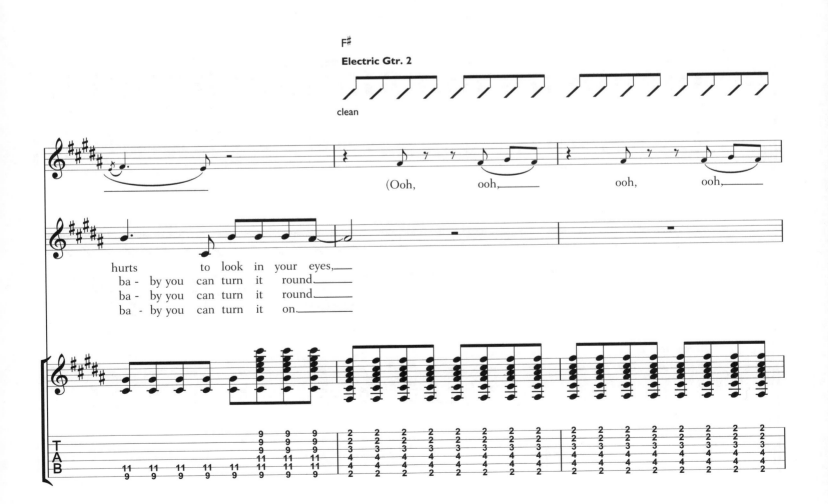

46

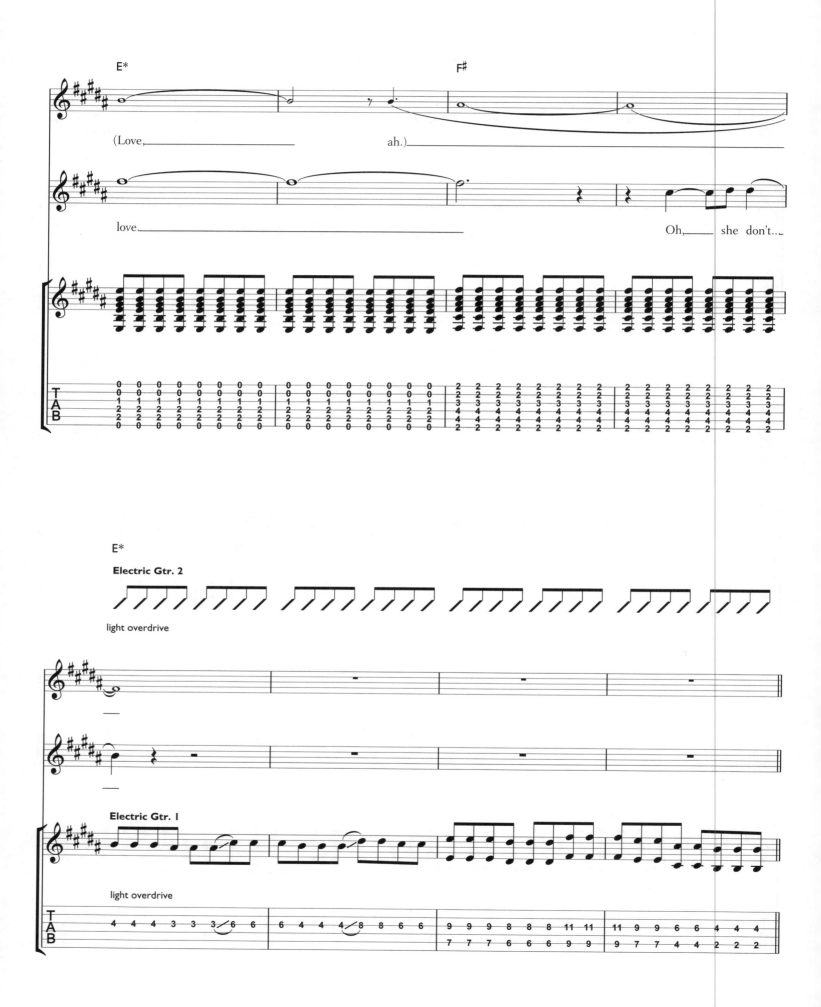

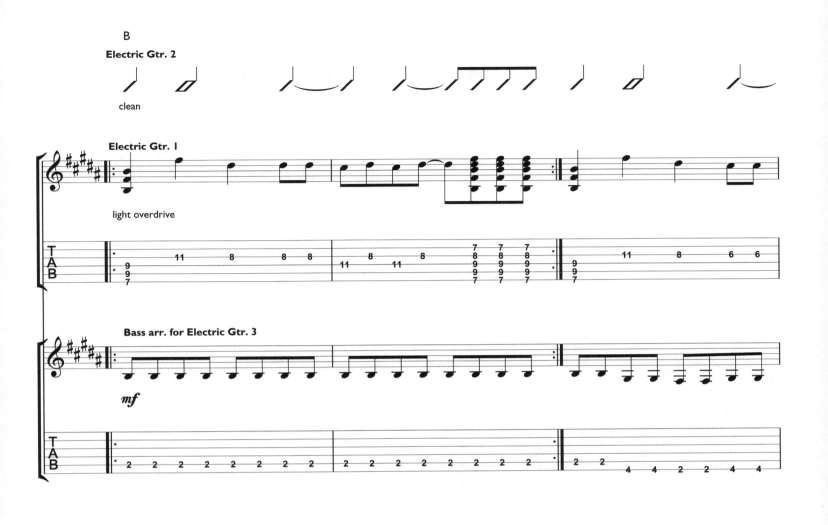

WHICH WAY TO HAPPY

Words and Music by Romeo Stodart

A-wake all you sleep-y heads,_ I come a crawl - ing.___

The last on the road___ be the first___ to be heard.___ And

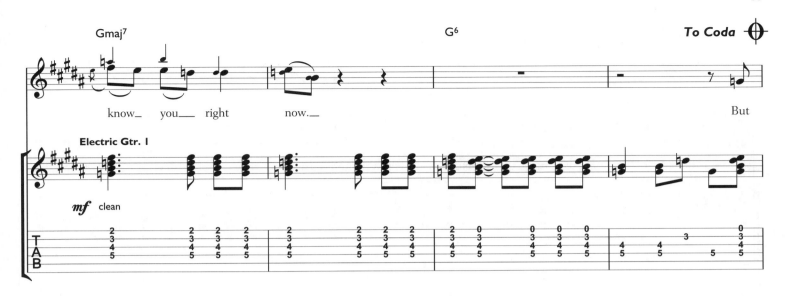

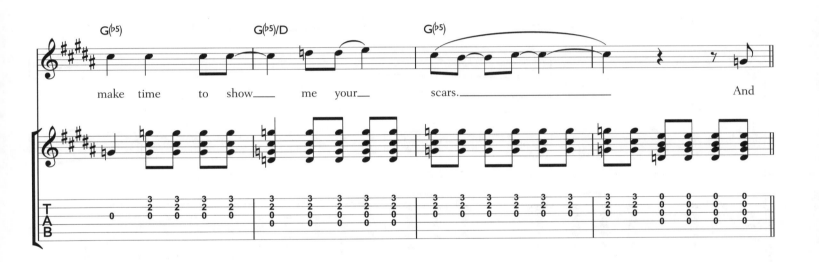

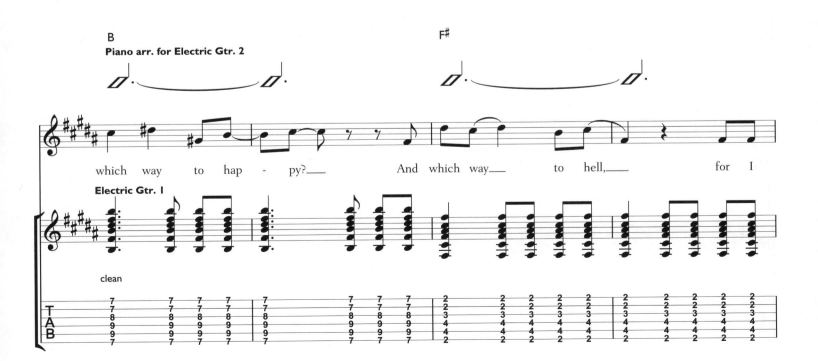

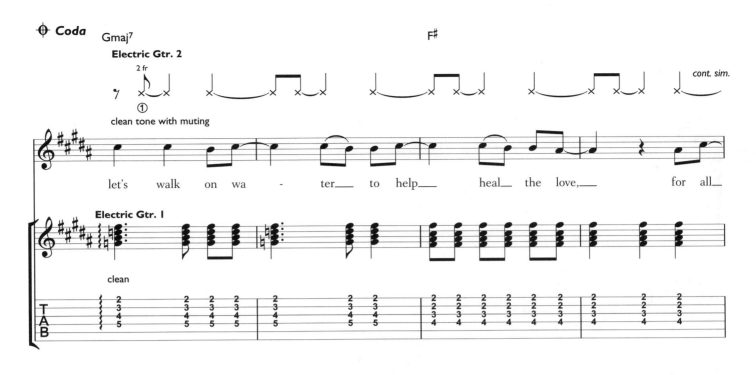

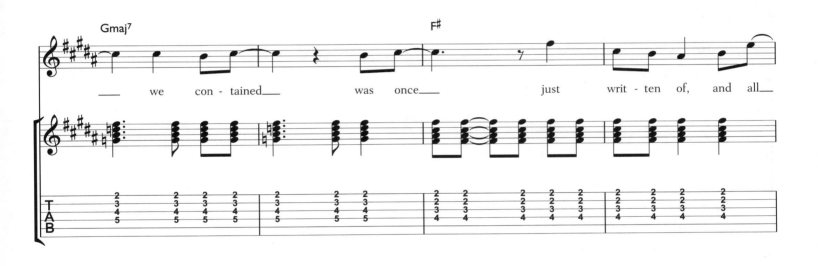

58

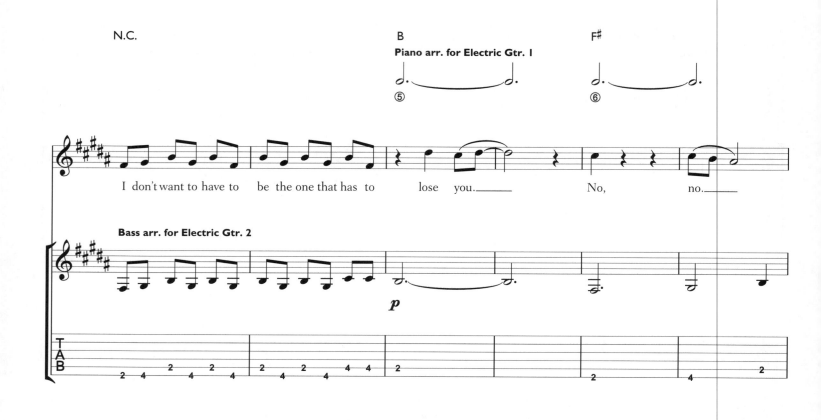

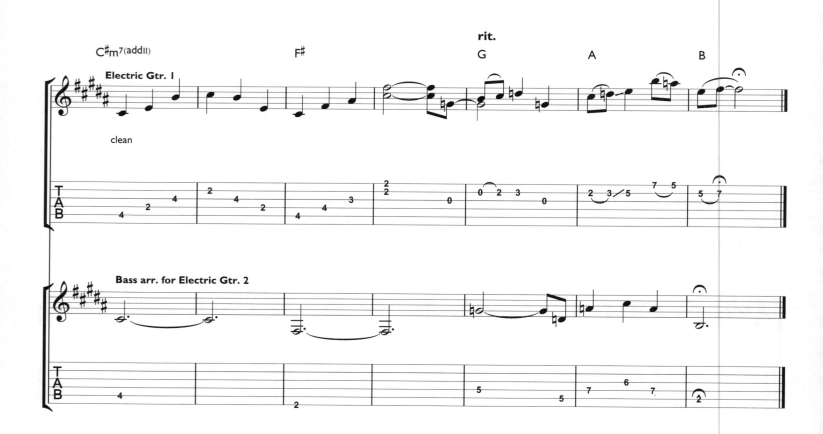

I SEE YOU, YOU SEE ME

Words and Music by Romeo Stodart

reverb and some sustain

DON'T GIVE UP THE FIGHT

Words and Music by Romeo Stodart

THIS LOVE

Words and Music by Romeo Stodart

E

left when I should - 've be - lieved that I could of held
— of my words were with - held_____ and un - heard I did

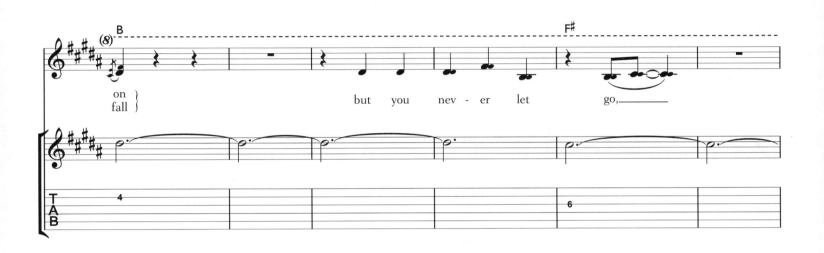

B   F#

on }
fall }   but you nev - er let   go,_____

$Esus^{2(add\#11)}$

or_ at least I don't think so._____

Acoustic Gtr. I   (Last 2 bars of Fig. I)

84

WHEELS ON FIRE

Words and Music by Romeo Stodart and Michele Stodart

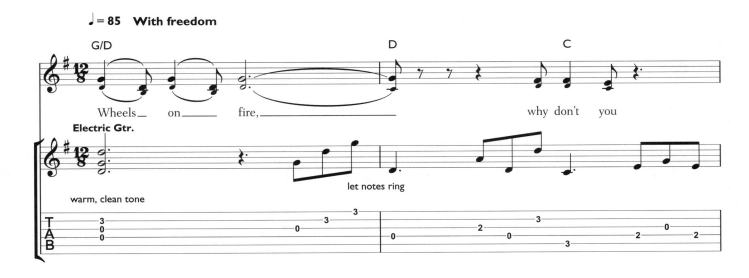

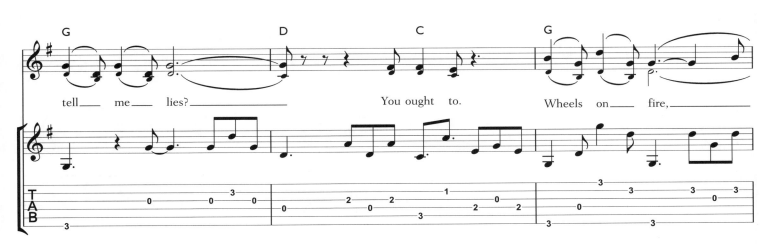

LOVE'S A GAME

Words and Music by Romeo Stodart

94

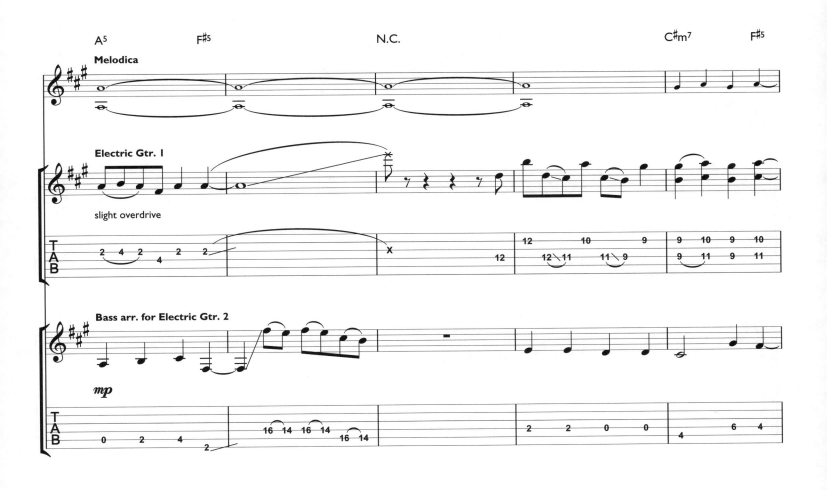

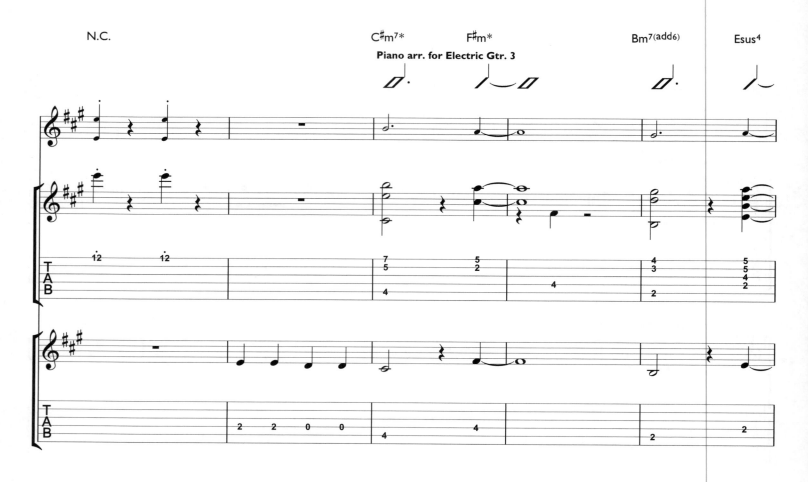

TRY

Words and Music by Romeo Stodart

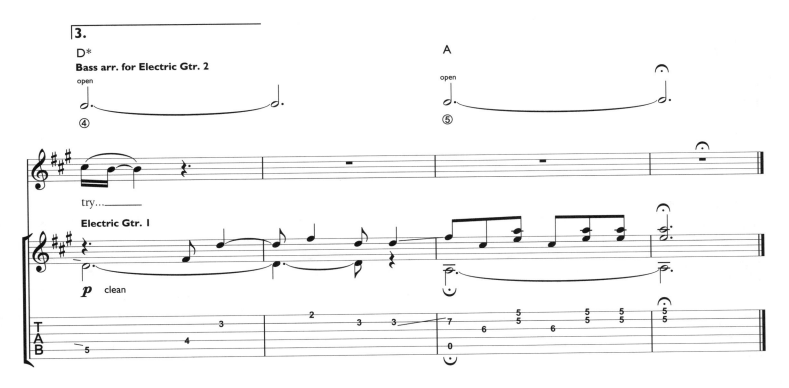

HYMN FOR HER

Words and Music by Romeo Stodart

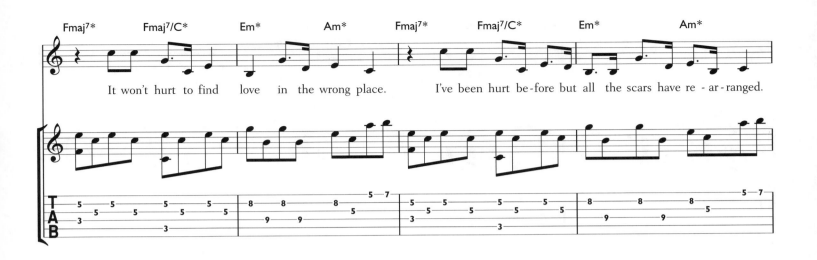

It won't hurt to find love in the wrong place. I've been hurt be-fore but all the scars have re - ar -ranged.

It won't hurt to choose a path that we all__ walk a - lone.

Chimes arr. for Gtr.

Electric Gtr.

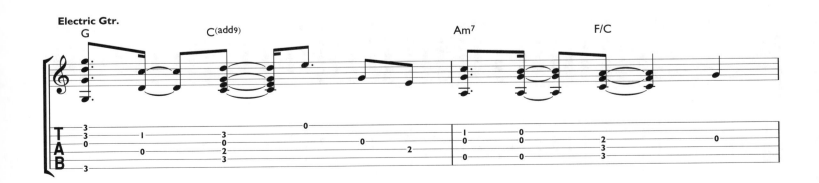

1,3. (Oh)__ when you love__ and you love__ and it ne - ver lies.
2,4. (Oh)__ when you love__ and you love__ and it ne - ver dies.

Ooh__ Hymn for__ Her.____

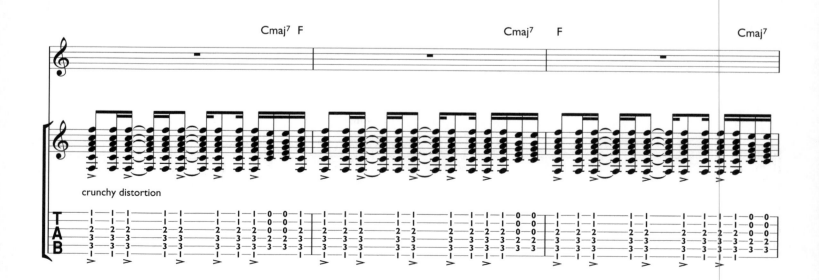

crunchy distortion

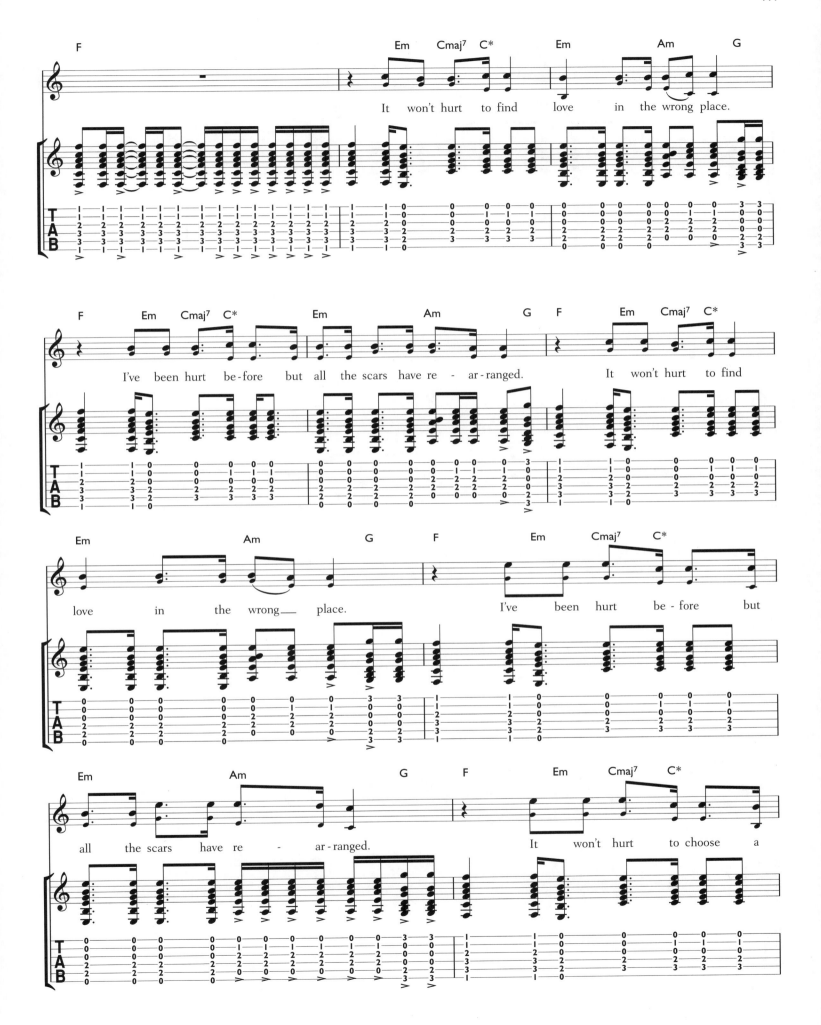

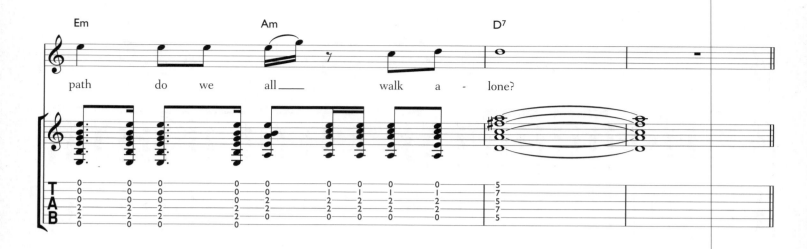

path   do   we   all___   walk   a - lone?

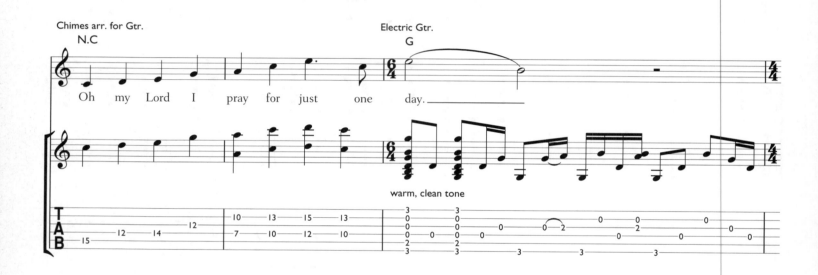

Chimes arr. for Gtr.

Oh   my   Lord   I   pray   for   just   one   day.___

warm, clean tone

Chimes arr. for Gtr.

Love   or   loathe   I   need   to   feel   a - gain.

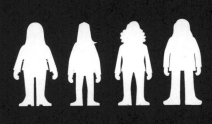